LEONARD BASKIN · THE GRAPHIC WORK · 1950 · 1970

Photograph by Jonathan Unger

LEONARD BASKIN

THE GRAPHIC WORK

1950 · 1970

FAR GALLERY
746 MADISON AVE.
NEW YORK · N · Y ·

MCMLXX

PREFACE
The FAR Gallery, on the occasion of celebrating its thirty-fifth year in the field of Fine Arts, is privileged to offer the current exhibition of two decades of the graphic work of Leonard Baskin. We are no less privileged to present this catalogue. Though far from illustrating all of the artist's works it will most adequately indicate the impressive range of his talent—a talent which embraces mastery of the artisan's tools harnessed to the service of a poetic and deeply personal philosophy and ideology. ❧ Leonard Baskin is capable of speaking most aptly for himself, whether in prose, the graphic media or any other art-form he elects to employ. His pen can be as incisive as his sharpest burin or graver, his rhetoric as subtle as the tones and gradations of his aquatints. ❧ On the 21st of May 1969, in the course of accepting the award of the Gold Medal for Graphic Art presented by The National Institute of Arts and Letters, Mr. Baskin remarked, "It is the special province of the Graphic Arts to be tendentious, to excoriate, attack and denounce (even rarely to praise), inventing scarifying images with specific and immediate purport". Leonard Baskin then points to the *oeuvre* of Goya, Kollwitz, Rouault, Grosz and Shahn. Surely Baskin takes his place in the "line" of these distinguished masters. ❧ But I would like to call attention to the phrase within parenthesis in the excerpt cited above "even rarely to praise". For in this exhibition of graphic works if the viewer will examine the small engravings or etchings of flora and fauna he will find that Leonard Baskin does indeed praise in the spirit of poets like Blake and Burns and Wordsworth and Meredith. He depicts a dragonfly, a toad or a thistle with the tenderness and perception which we may observe in Lautrec and Picasso when they choose, too, "to praise". ❧ The publication of this catalogue was made feasible by the kindness of many and the Herculean efforts of a dedicated few. May I here express thanks and appreciation? ❧ Examples of Leonard Baskin's works long "out of print" were loaned to this exhibition by Mrs. Ann Ratner; Mr. Herman Shickman; Mr. Sylvan Cole, director of the Associated American Artists Gallery; Mr. Abe Lublin of A. Lublin Inc.; Mr. Harold Hugo, The Meriden Gravure Company; Mr. and Mrs. Leonard Baskin; and Mr.

and Mrs. John E. Marqusee. ❧ To all the staff of The Meriden Gravure Company who performed so valiantly our deep gratitude is here expressed. Also to Charles W. Yeiser of the FAR Gallery who served as an efficient catalyst to fuse the various efforts. ❧ Special thanks is due Dale Roylance, Curator of Graphic Arts at Yale University, who provided this superb introduction for the present catalogue.

Herman J. Wechsler, Director
FAR Gallery

In the twenty-three years since his earliest dated print—a most apt and prophetic wood engraving of a "Man with Graphic Tools"—Leonard Baskin has emerged as one of the most significantly representative graphic artists of our time. This preeminence has been won not only with the success of his incisive graphic statements of the condition and image of man in the twentieth century, but also in his lonely refusal to depart either from the art historical tradition of representational imagery or from the great continuum of tradition in the printing arts of the last five centuries. ❧ Whether as draughtsman, sculptor, printmaker, book designer or illustrator, Baskin states and restates, affirms and reaffirms his ardent belief in the essential worth and dignity of man. Each of his simultaneous creative careers, and the prolific number of drawings, sculptures, prints and books they have produced, underline the faith of this pervasive theme. Surrounding this pure truth in Baskin's art, like a Temptation of Saint Anthony, swarm all the many Baskin devils, figures of corruption, night birds, and the graphic apparitions of evil and death. ❧ This distinctive Baskin iconography, in an age of desperate iconoclasm, gives his work an intensely personal subjectivity unusual in modern art. Thus have the flayed Everyman, the Angel of Death, the grim armoured warrior, the ugly dog, the uglier crow more claw than wing, the fat poet laureate, the man of torment with head-perched night bird, the hanged man, the sinister insects, the owls and pomegranates, become the personal repertory of images inimitably Baskin's own. ❧ An exhibition of the prints of Leonard Baskin offers the opportunity to observe the chronological genesis of several of these various motifs repeated throughout Baskin's art. As a counter theme it is also possible to see a marked change in sophistication of technique from the early, tentative wood engraving experiments with white line and the multiple graver to the later mastery of the most elaborate engraved line and texture. As early examples, two wood engraved prints of the late 1940's, "Lovers" and "Three Nude Men", still betray a young artist's search for his own style. The *Little Book of Natural History*, 1952, has the distinction of being the first true edition of Baskin's now famous

Gehenna Press.* The still early wood and linocuts of this little portfolio have a certain charm, but, except for the bristling porcupine, show little promise of Baskin's later technical and stylistic finesse. It is characteristic of the innate consistency of Baskin's mixture of art and intellect, however, that his first Gehenna book should be this primitivistic version of a woodcut bestiary. The format of early printed books as a point of departure for his own expressive style in bookmaking is a fascinating aspect of many of Baskin's Gehenna Press books. The medieval bestiary is the general source of inspiration for *A Little Book of Natural History*; Hooke's *Micrographia*, 1665, is the specific source of the book's woodcut of a huge flea. Such borrowings are not uncongenial to Baskin's art. Other early printed picture books, particularly in the natural sciences, will play an increasingly important influence in his style and subject matter. The Kafkaesque vision of insect as monster is our modern reaction to the album of Baskin etchings and engravings of *Horned Beetles and Other Insects*, Gehenna Press, 1958. But Baskin's elegant and precise plates, while rendering the quiet ferocity of these insects, are more directly inspired by the color plate books of early entomology illustrated by Maria Sybille Merrian and other seventeenth-century artists. ✍ It is possible to discover other marvelous relationships between Baskin's modern books and graphics and the secrets of old picture books. The artist's great fascination with historical anatomy books is evident in his extensive collection of these atlases, and his almost antiquarian expertise of such books. In his art, the flayed anatomy has become like a Baskin signature. As early as 1952 his woodcuts begin to take on a texture of vivisection. His prints of blind men, and a small "Day of Atonement" that is the germinal image of the large "Stra-

---

* Baskin's unusual love of books and printing is, at least in part, the product of an otherwise barren, for him, two years' experience as a student in the Yale Art School. He freely admits his dismissal from Yale, for "incorrigible insubordination", but also gives grateful credit to the amenities of the environment at Yale. Baskin spent much of his time with reading and discovering books at the Yale Library and printing on the hand press available to students in Jonathan Edwards College. Both of these early activities have flowered into lifelong preoccupations. A measure of the stimulus may be seen in Baskin's present fine rare book library and his proprietorship of one of the best of existing private presses. As for Yale, Baskin is now a trustee of the Yale University Library Associates and an archive of Gehenna Press printing is an important part of the library's Graphic Arts Collection.

bismic Jew", are early versions. In the 1953 "Man with Forsythia" and the "Man with Spring Plants" the forms become true modern *ecorché* anatomy figures, but display abstracted interior landscapes full of entangled winter branches and searching roots rather than circulatory or nervous systems. Yet the uneradicable suggestion remains of the lift-up anatomy plates of antique medical books. ❧ The technique of these first largely conceived prints is bold yet full of graphic nuance. The sixteenth-century engraving technique of white dot *criblé*, and lines of every calligraphic calibration fill these interior wood engraved spaces. Enlarged in imaginative detail, we have Franz Kline black on white abstractions. Reduced, we discover an organic essence created by the artist for these interior forms, like the hair-root filled crevices of a plant lifted from an outgrown pot. The calligraphic quality of line and serenity of mood implied in the "Man with Forsythia" print become consummate realizations in one of Baskin's greatest woodcut prints, the "Tobias and the Angel" of 1958. Here the black line achieves an embrace of exterior and interior form that is almost sculptural. The poetry of the narrative moment is also beautifully realized in this print. ❧ The serene peace of these early "anatomical" prints such as the "Tobias" and "Man with Forsythia" is shattered in later excoriated figures by Baskin. These life size hanged men and near cadavers are not only flayed but blood streaked and disemboweled. Full of anguish and torment, they seem transfixed between their last dying shriek and the quiet of death. The huge woodcuts of "The Hydrogen Man", 1954, "The Hanged Man", 1955, "The Torment", 1958, the drawing and sculpture of "Glutted Death", 1958, and the drawings and woodcuts of "The Angel of Death" are all disquieting on first encounter. But the aesthetic detachment inherent in the graphic image lends a magical power of exorcism even to the most frightening of events. In truth we must see in these images of death by Baskin soul-gripping, modern manifestations of one of the most ancient and traditional of graphic images. And again we find Baskin as traditionalist revivifying ancient book and print images. From medieval times manuscripts and woodcuts have presented the cadaverous figure of Death and his escapeless victims. The Dance of Death, the *Ars Moriendi, Danse Macabre* or *Totentanz* have had countless graphic versions from Blockbooks to Holbein, Rowlandson to Baskin. With this awareness—a kind of solace from history and the library—we look at the Angel of Death again. The awful edge of stridency in the Baskin woodcuts seems quieter. The anxious first confrontation becomes the waitful acceptance demanded of Everyman, then and now. ๛ Other Baskin reconciliation with the visage of death is seen in his appreciation of the historical death-mask. He has created countless prints after the famous Deville mask of William Blake, and has found somber but fascinating influence in the pages of Benkard's treatise on death-masks, *Das Ewige Antlitz*. To those souls immune to any inner peace with such an idea, who find this interest ghoulish, Baskin also offers a group of spectral images in his prints and sculptures that sheds all tranquility. ๛ Like a recurring nightmare is the baleful hound that repeatedly confronts us in Baskin's art. This bloated image of uncaged hostility, with its staggeringly sardonic title of "Love me, love my dog", appears as drawing in 1957, sculpture in 1958, and woodcut in 1959. The dog as an ultimate specter of evil is Cerberus, three headed guardian to the gate of Hell. Baskin's recent set of illustrations to Dante's *Divine Comedy* includes his own version of Cerberus as a demoniacal, triple-threat "Love me, love my dog", as well as other menacing Hounds of Hell. Any personal prejudice against dogs is disproved by Baskin's own well loved pet dog, although she has been somewhat perversely named "Rabbit". Baskin's persistently unflattering image of the species may be a remnant of a Talmudic antipathy; certainly his wonderfully gross depictions of the *Castle Street Dogs*, Gehenna Press, 1953, disturbs at least one previously inviolate American icon. Other street scenes in Baskin's Worcester period woodcuts also have the same scrawny-legged, homely-faced dogs loitering about. The fastidious dog lover will find only one exception to the Cerberus and sad strays of Castle Street, an elegant, cameo-like design of the Borzoi Hound, which Baskin created as a wood engraving for Knopf Publishers in 1957. ๛ William Blake's *Auguries of Innocence*, Gehenna Press, 1959, is one of Baskin's triumphs as book designer and illustrator, and has special interest here for its indicative inclusion of several of Baskin's most often repeated images. The owl, used repeatedly by Baskin as an emblematic press-mark and print image, appears with Blake's lines: "The Owl that calls upon the Night / speaks the Unbeliever's Fright"; the fat poet laureate, one of Baskin's best images, appears, but in masquerade as Caesar, with the lines: "The strongest poison ever known / came from Caesar's laurel Crown"; the dog, with tiny eyes and bloated tongue: "A Dog starv'd at his Master's Gate / predicts the ruin of the State"; and the armoured warrior, used as sculpture and print at other times, appears here with Blake's lines: "Naught can deform the Human Race / like to the Armourer's Iron Brace". ❧ The kinship of Blake and Baskin is very strong, and Baskin has found an inexhaustible source of inspiration in the works of this great artist-poet. Even a reverent self-identification with Blake is not impossible. Both artists do not disdain the power of illustration as a vehicle of expression, and share a respect, unusual in art, for the combined word and image. Other impudent parallels are possible. The great English artist-poet had his own group of repeated images, was mystically oriented towards the archetypal problems of evil and death, created his own style out of the main stream of tradition, and throughout his life preferred the expressive power of books and printing to the more prestigious art of easel painting. In his turn Baskin has created his own iconography using traditional roots, made significant graphic statements of man's near-imponderable problems of evil and death, created his own style yet remained tradition oriented, and has always disdained oil painting in his vast preference for the graphic arts. If Baskin's imagery seems harsh, even chaotic in contrast to Blake's ordered and graceful line, this may be one contrast of the eighteenth and twentieth centuries. Comparisons remain odious, and are unfair when one artist has achieved something like artistic godhood; they will be very flattering to a still young artist never known for his modesty. But the final comparison remains most effective in its illumination of both Blake's and Baskin's single-minded devotion to the beauty of the theme of man as image. Innumerable ringing quotations from Blake are possible here; one from Baskin will suffice: "Our human frame, our gutted mansion, our enveloping sack of beef and ash, is yet a glory. Glorious in defining our universal sodality, and glorious in defining our utter uniqueness. The human figure is the image of all men and of one man. It contains all and can express all".

Dale Roylance
Curator of Graphic Arts
Yale University Library

CATALOGUE

1.
LEONARD BASKIN—LB AET 29
Woodcut
21×18.   1952

2.
PIG IS FORBIDDEN TO THEE.
Woodcut.
18¾×25.   1952

3.
TWO BLIND MEN
Wood engraving.
7¾×4⅞.   1952

4.
MAN OF PEACE.
Woodcut.
62×31.   1952

5.
VIEW OF WORCESTER.
Wood engraving.
10×8⅝.   1953

6.
MAN WITH SPRING PLANTS.
Wood engraving.
13⅝×5⅝.   1953

7.
TORMENTED MAN.
Woodcut.
17×19.   1953

8.
HYDROGEN MAN.
Woodcut.
62×31.   1954

9.
SORROWING AND TERRIFIED MAN.
Woodcut.
36″ diameter.   1955

10.
BEATITUDE.
Wood engraving.
10⅛×15.   1955

11.
THE STRABISMIC JEW.
Woodcut.
41×23.   1955

12.
WALT WHITMAN.
Wood engraving.
14×3⅞.   1955

13.
THE HANGED MAN.
Woodcut.
67×23.   1955

14.
THE POET LAUREATE.
Woodcut.
23×48.   1955

15.
HAMAN.
Woodcut.
48×23.   1956

16.
BORZOI.
Wood engraving.
¾×1¾.   1957

17.
DYING STAG.
Wood engraving.
3 ½×3 ⅛.   1957

18.
BOAR.
Wood engraving.
2⅝×5⅝.   1957

19.
ENVY.
Wood engraving.
3 ¼″ diameter.   1958

20.
DOG.
Wood engraving.
4×6 ½.   1958

21.
RANATRA AMERICANA.
Etching.
4 ½×3 ¾.   1958

22.
LUCANNUS CERVUS.
Etching.
4 ½×3 ¼.   1958

23.
TOBIAS AND THE ANGEL.
Wood engraving.
15×15.   1958

24.
TORMENT.
Woodcut.
31×23.   1958

25.
LOVE ME LOVE MY DOG.
Wood engraving.
7 ¼×6 ⅛.   1958

26.
DEATH AMONG THE THISTLES.
Wood engraving.
6×8.   1959

27.
ANGEL OF DEATH.
Woodcut.
62×31.   1959

28.
DEATH OF THE POET LAUREATE.
Wood engraving.
11 ¾″ diameter.   1959

29.
EVERYMAN.
Woodcut.
83×23.   1960

30.
SUCCOTH.
Woodcut.
20×15.   1960

31.
PASSOVER.
Woodcut.
19⅝×15⅛.   1960

32.
JEREMIAH.
Woodcut.
29⅜×13⅛.   1961

33.
SACRIFICE OF ISAAC.
17×15⅛.   1961

34.
MOSES.
Woodcut.
14⅞×15¾.   1961

35.
LEONARD BASKIN—AET 42.
Woodcut.
32×23 ½.   1962

36.
AUGUSTE RODIN.
Lithograph.
$19\frac{7}{8} \times 19\frac{3}{8}$.   1963

37.
ANDREA MANTEGNA.
Etching.
$17\frac{1}{4} \times 14\frac{3}{4}$.   1963

38.
FRANCISCO DE GOYA.
Etching.
$17\frac{3}{4} \times 14\frac{3}{4}$.   1963

39.
ERNST BARLACH.
Etching.
$17\frac{1}{4} \times 14\frac{3}{4}$.   1963

40.
HERCULES SEGHERS.
Etching.
$17\frac{1}{4} \times 14\frac{1}{4}$.   1963

41.
WILLIAM BLAKE.
Etching.
$17\frac{1}{4} \times 14\frac{3}{4}$.   1963

42.
BIRD IN THE SUN.
Etching.
$8 \times 9\frac{7}{8}$.   1964

43.
EDVARD MUNCH.
Etching.
11¾×17¼.   1964

44.
ROGER VAN DER WEYDEN.
Etching.
17¾×17½.   1964

45.
D. H. AND J. HOPFER.
Etching.
14¾×17¼.   1964

46.
ADOLF VON MENZEL.
Etching.
17¾×17¼.   1964

47.
JUSEPE DE RIBERA.
Etching.
17¾×14½.   1964

48.
THOMAS EAKINS.
Etching.
17⅞×13¼.   1964

49.
THOMAS EAKINS.
Woodcut.
31¾×23½.   1965

50.
FLEDGELING.
Etching.
12 1/2 × 8 7/8.   1966

51.
DOG IN THE MEADOW.
Etching.
15 × 8 5/8.   1966

52.
SPREAD EAGLE.
Etching.
8 7/8 × 12 1/2.   1966

53.
ICARUS.
Woodcut.
32 × 21 1/2.   1967

54.
BENEVOLENT ANGEL.
Etching.
17 3/4 × 17 1/2.   1967

55.
THE SHERIFF.
Etching.
17 3/4 × 17 1/2.   1967

56.
MUMMY.
Etching.
22 1/2 × 17 1/2.   1968

57.
AGONIZED.
Woodcut.
29 ½ × 23 ¼.   1969

58.
MERRIAN.
Etching.
17¾ × 14¾.   1969

59.
MONTICELLI.
Etching.
17¾ × 17⅝.   1969

60.
GERICAULT.
Etching.
16¾ × 13¾.   1969

61.
FUSELI.
Lithograph.
20½ × 14⅜.   1969

62.
BETRAYAL.
Woodcut.
32 × 27.   1969

63.
MIASMAL.
Etching.
17¾ × 11¾.   1969

64.
DISTENTION.
Etching.
35 ½ × 13 ⅝.   1969

65.
OEDIPUS AT COLONUS.
Etching.
23 ⅝ × 17 ½.   1969.

66.
BIRDMAN.
Etching.
17¾ × 23¾.   1969

67.
BIRDMAN WITH SPREAD WINGS.
Etching.
11⅞ × 17⅞.   1969

68.
BETRAYED.
Etching.
21¾ × 27¾.   1969

69.
THEODULE RIBOT.
Wood engraving.
3 × 4⅞.   1969

70.
GEORGE MINNE.
Wood engraving.
6⅜ × 4.   1969

71.
RODOLPHE BRESDIN.
Etching.
8¾×5¾.   1969

72.
J. F. MILLET AND TH. ROUSSEAU.
Wood engraving.
6¼×6½.   1969

73.
CAMILLE COROT.
Wood engraving.
7⅜×4⅝.   1969
(on cover)

74.
GREAT TEASEL.
Etching.
21⅝×27¾.   1969

PLATES

LB
ÆT 29

I. LEONARD BASKIN—LB AET 29

החזר לא תאכלז

2. PIG IS FORBIDDEN TO THEE

3. TWO BLIND MEN

4. MAN OF PEACE

5. VIEW OF WORCESTER

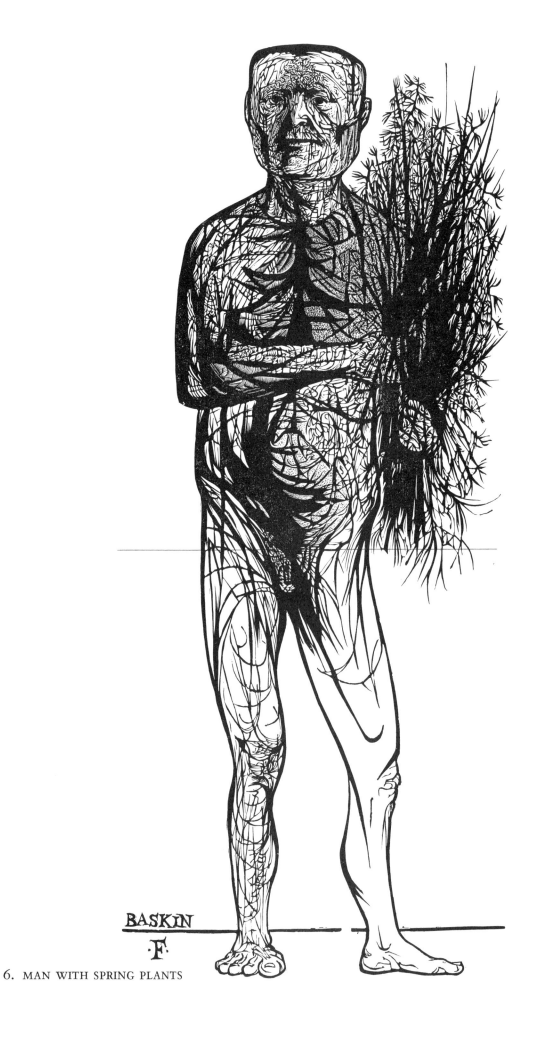

BASKIN
·F·

6. MAN WITH SPRING PLANTS

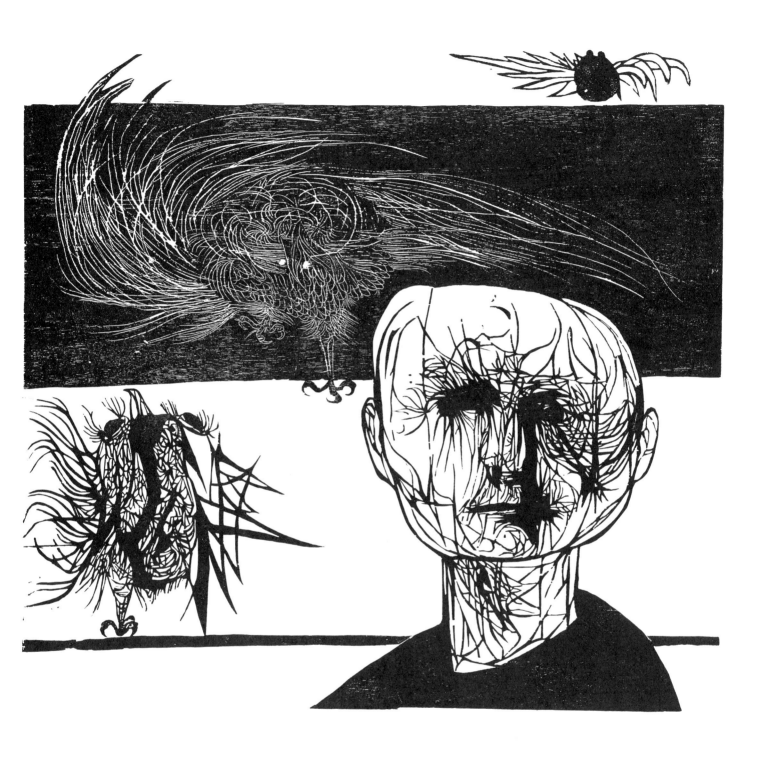

7. TORMENTED MAN

8. HYDROGEN MAN

9. SORROWING AND TERRIFIED MAN

IO. BEATITUDE

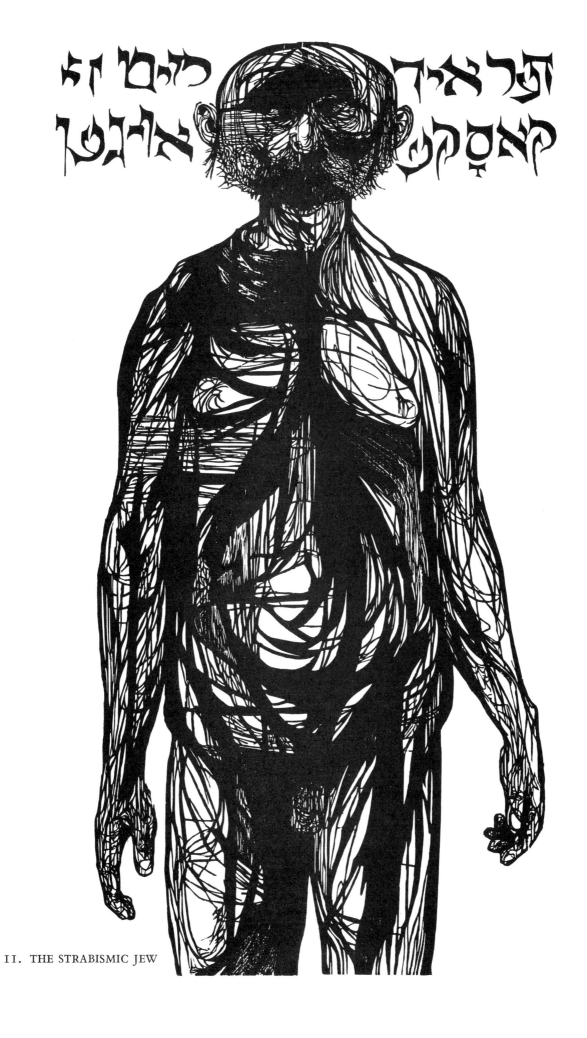

11. THE STRABISMIC JEW

I2. WALT WHITMAN

13. THE HANGED MAN

14. THE POET LAUREATE

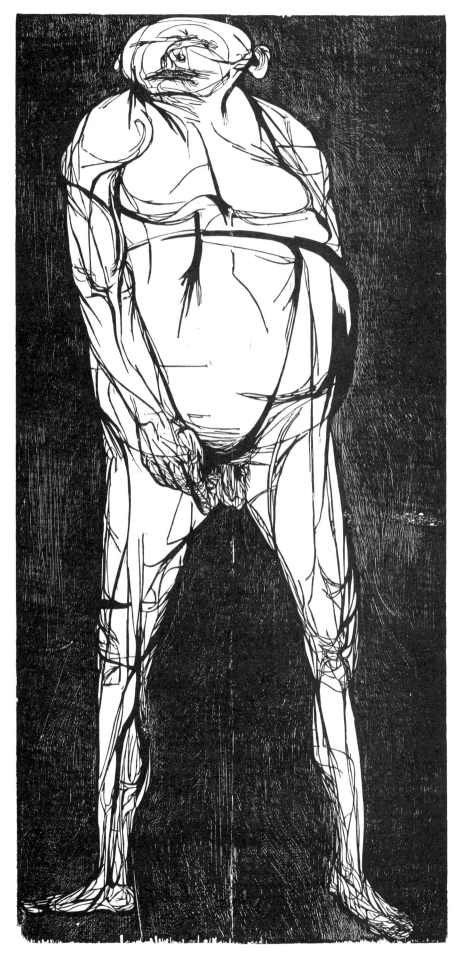

15. HAMAN

16. BORZOI

17. DYING STAG

18. BOAR

19. ENVY

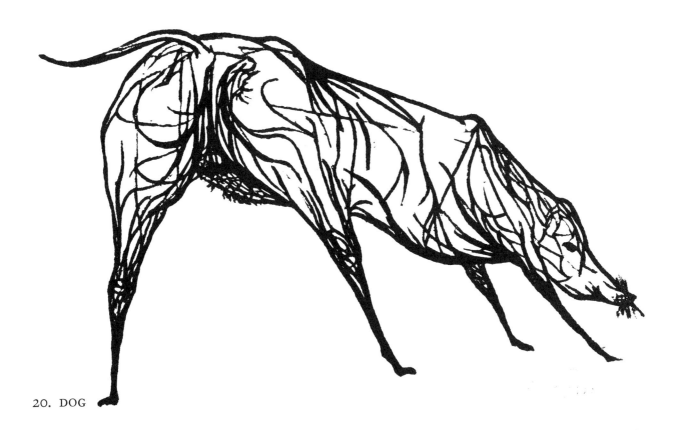

20. DOG

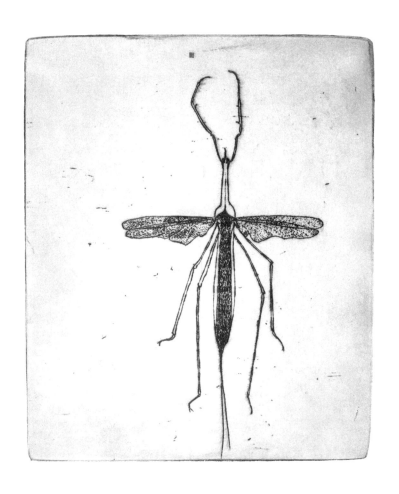

21. RANATRA AMERICANA

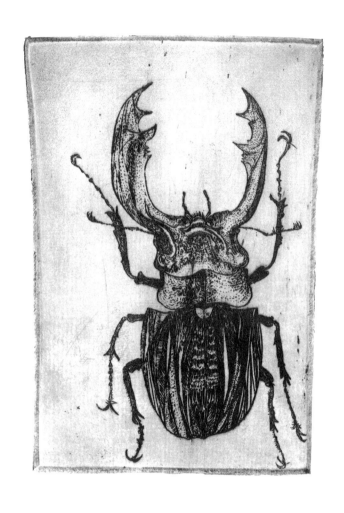

22. LUCANNUS CERVUS

23. TOBIAS AND THE ANGEL

24. TORMENT

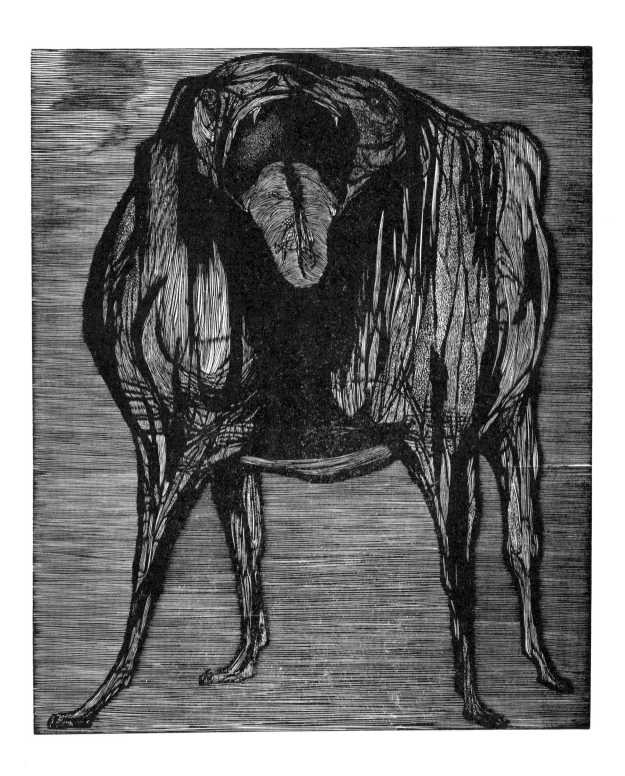

25. LOVE ME LOVE MY DOG

26. DEATH AMONG THE THISTLES

27. ANGEL OF DEATH

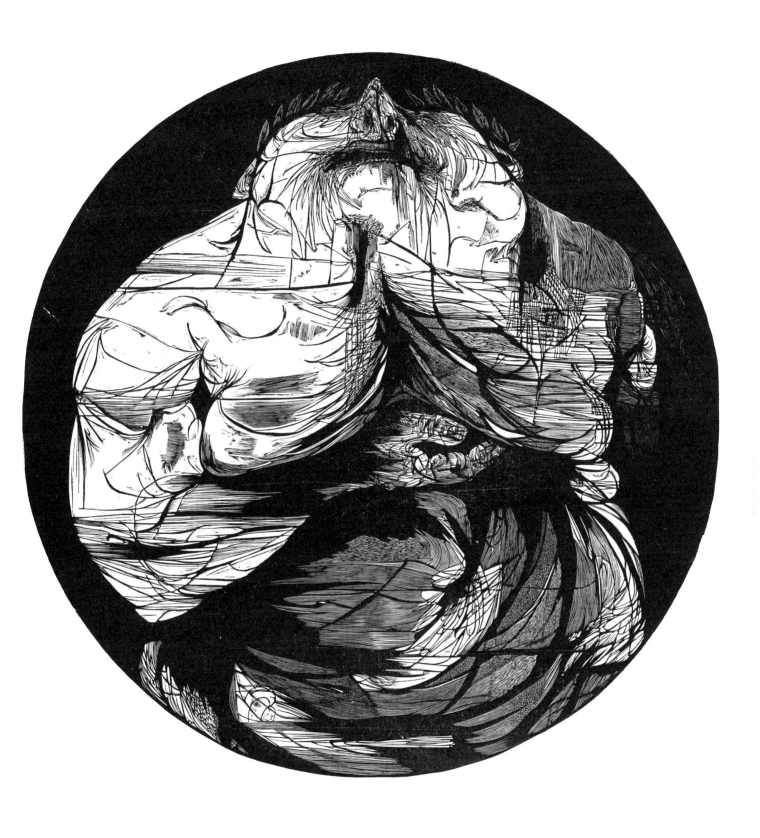

28. DEATH OF THE POET LAUREATE

29. EVERYMAN

חג הסכת תעשה לך שבעת ימים

30. SUCCOTH

פסח

31. PASSOVER

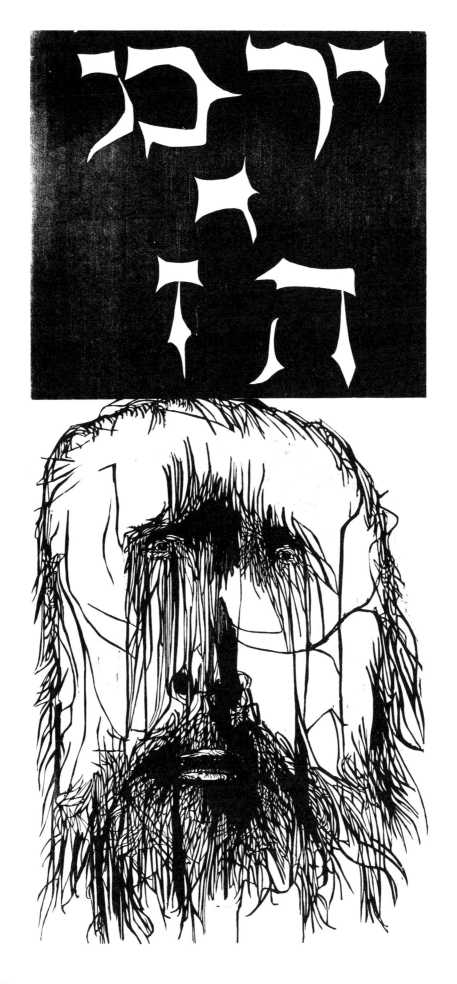

32. JEREMIAH

33. SACRIFICE OF ISAAC

4. MOSES

35. LEONARD BASKIN—AET 42

36. AUGUSTE RODIN

37. ANDREA MANTEGNA

38. FRANCISCO DE GOYA

39. ERNST BARLACH

40. HERCULES SEGHERS

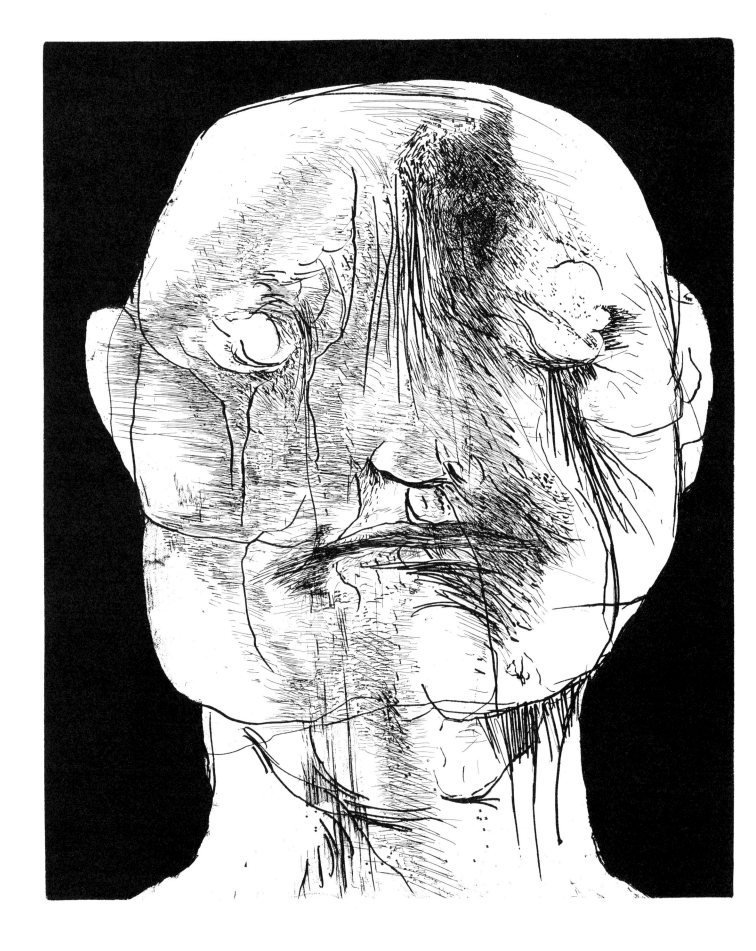

41. WILLIAM BLAKE

42. BIRD IN THE SUN

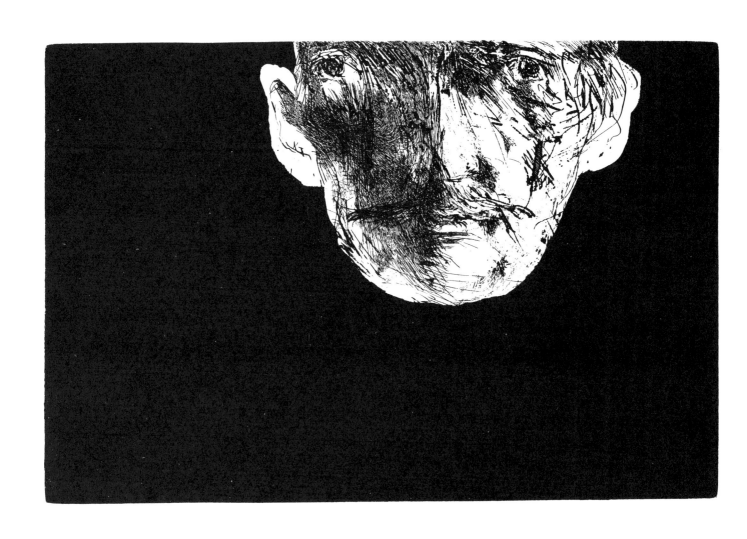

43. EDVARD MUNCH

44. ROGER VAN DER WEYDEN

45. D. H. AND J. HOPFER

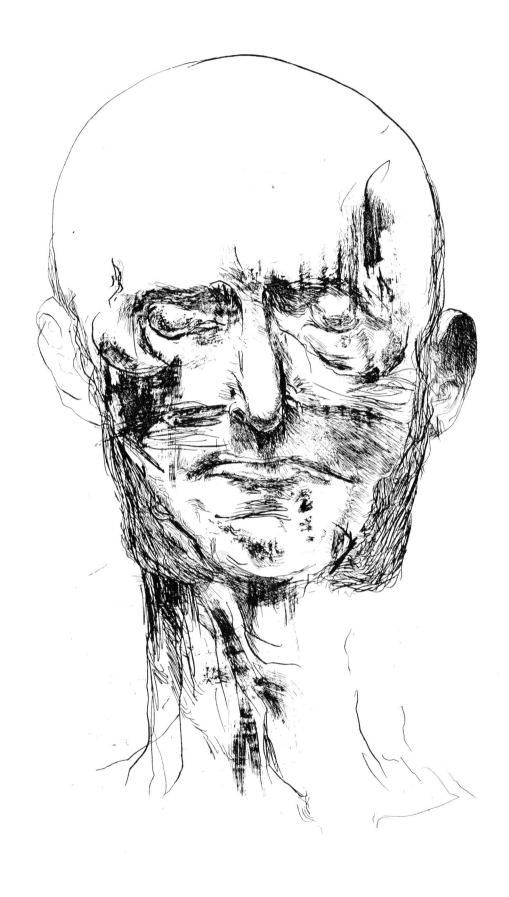

46. ADOLF VON MENZEL

47. JUSEPE DE RIBERA

48. THOMAS EAKINS

49. THOMAS EAKINS

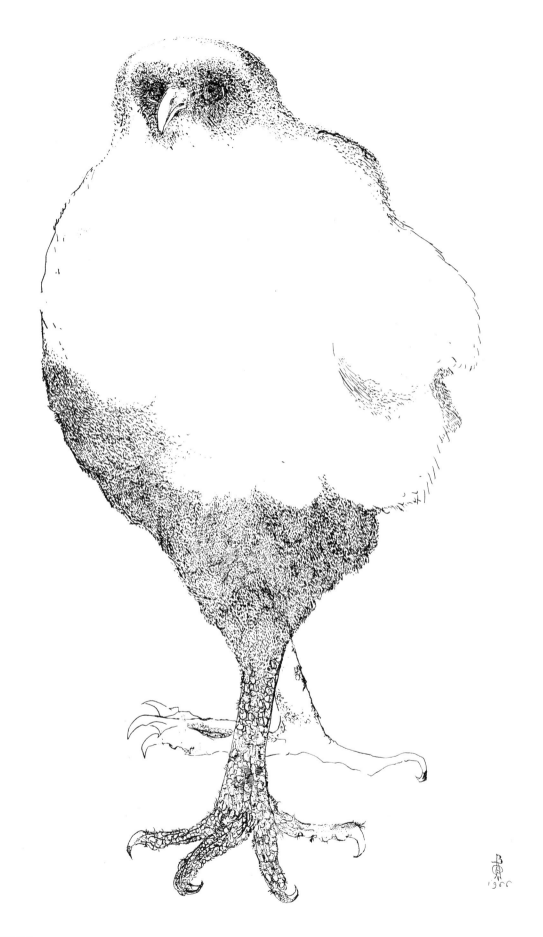

50. FLEDGELING

51. DOG IN THE MEADOW

52. SPREAD EAGLE

53. ICARUS

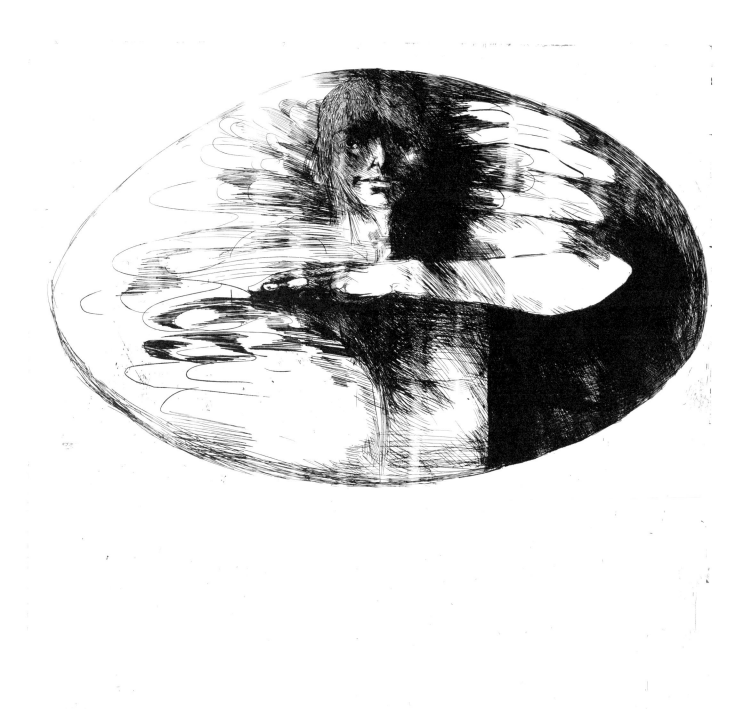

54. BENEVOLENT ANGEL

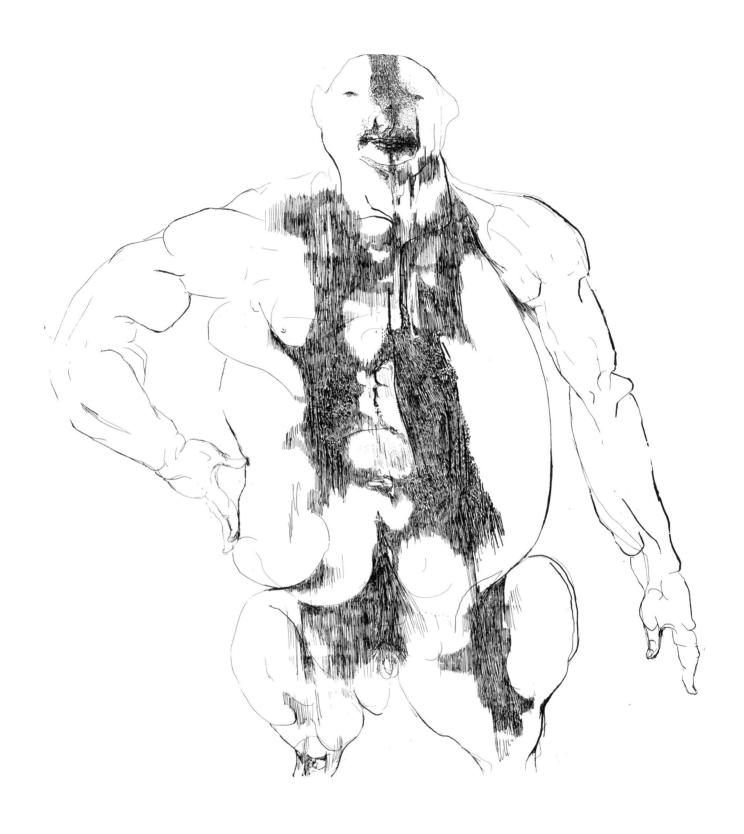

55. THE SHERIFF

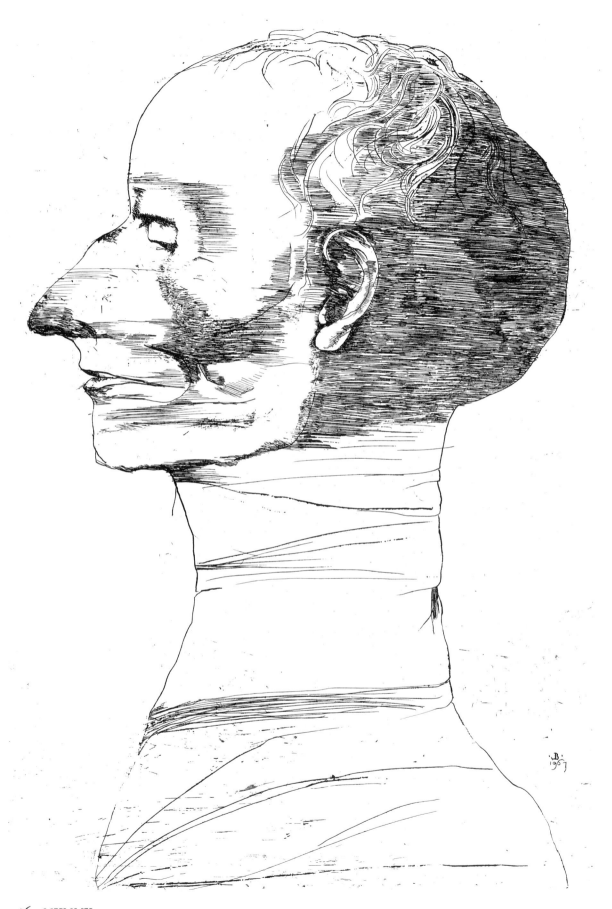

56. MUMMY

57. AGONIZED

58. MERRIAN

59. MONTICELLI

60. GERICAULT

61. FUSELI

62. BETRAYAL

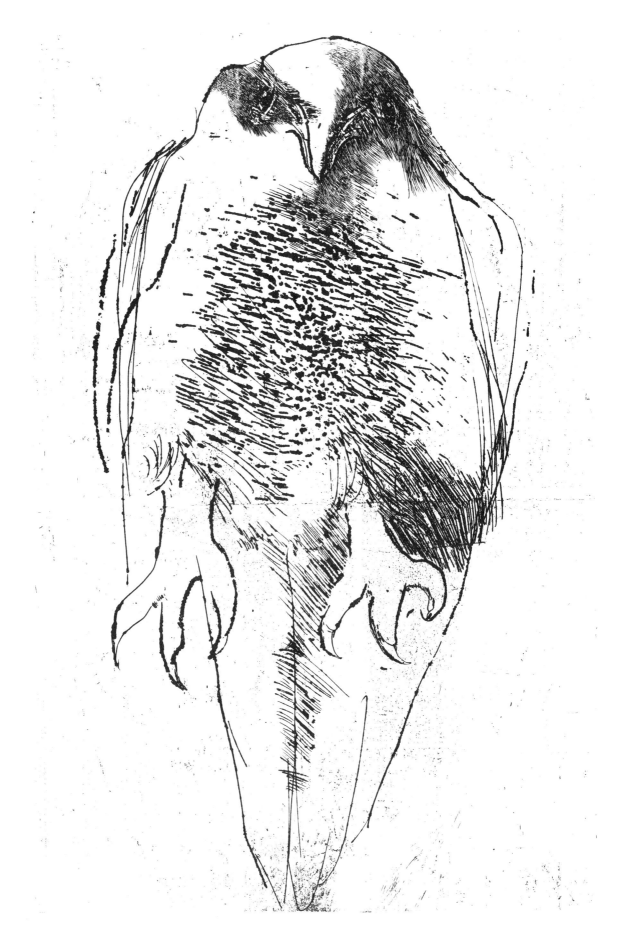

63. MIASMAL

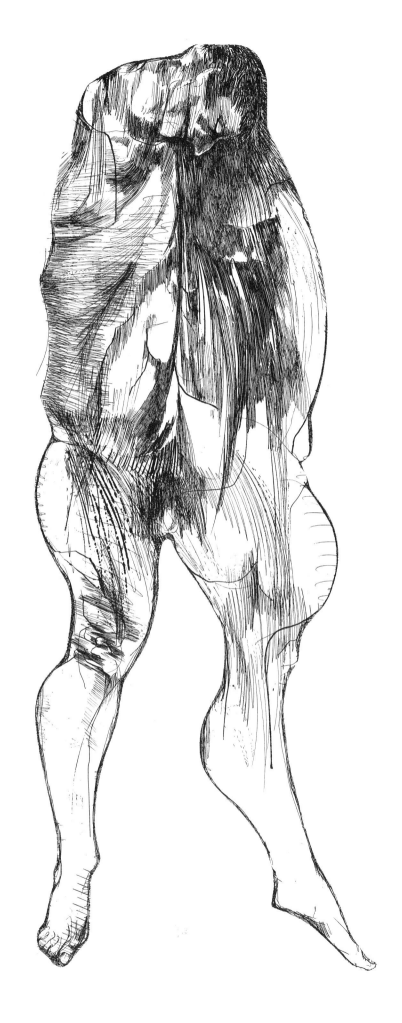

64. DISTENTION

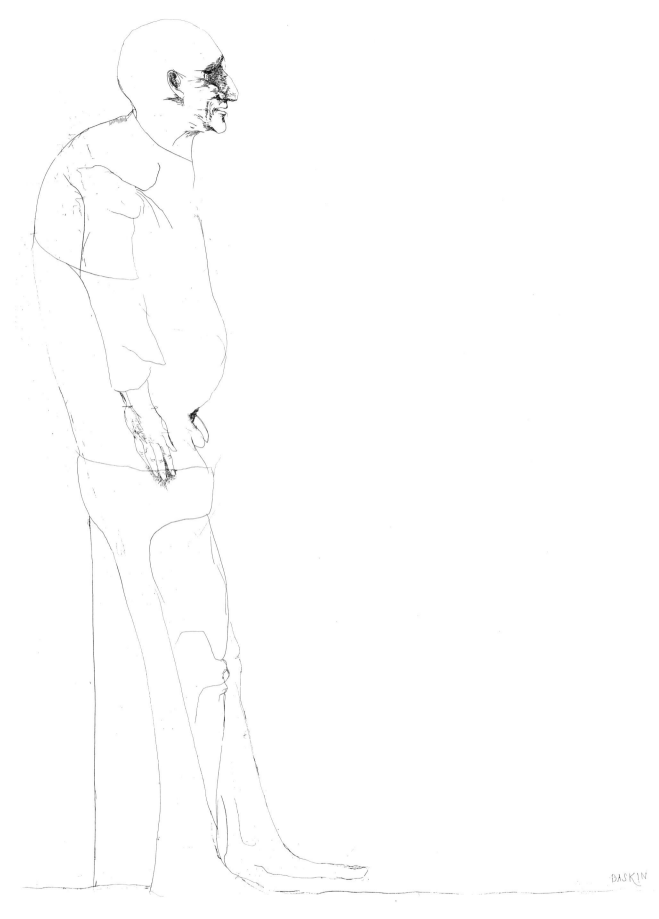

65. OEDIPUS AT COLONUS

66. BIRDMAN

67. BIRDMAN WITH SPREAD WINGS

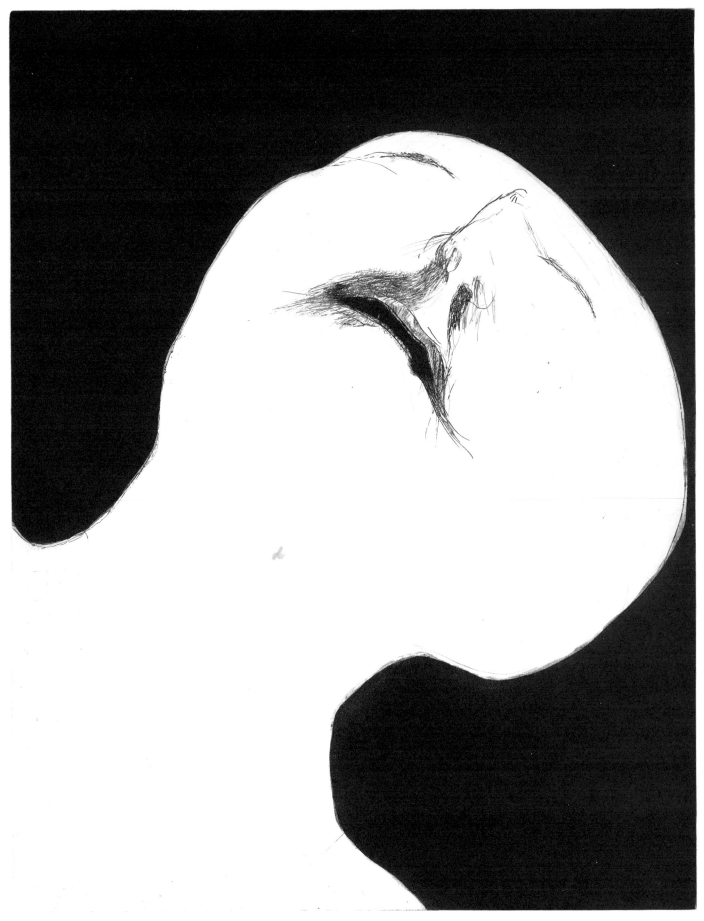

68. BETRAYED

69. THEODULE RIBOT

L

70. GEORGE MINNE

XII/c   Bresdin

71. RODOLPHE BRESDIN

72. J. F. MILLET AND TH. ROUSSEAU

73. CAMILLE COROT

74. GREAT TEASEL

EDUCATION

1937–1939, special studies with Maurice Glickman; 1939–1941, New York University School of Architecture and Allied Arts, New York; 1941–1943, Yale University School of Fine Arts; 1949, The New School for Social Research; 1950, Académie de la Grande Chaumière, Paris, France; 1951, Academy of Fine Arts, Florence, Italy

HONORS AND AWARDS

1940, Prix de Rome, Honorable Mention for Sculpture; 1941, Scholarship to Yale University School of Fine Art; 1947, Louis Comfort Tiffany Foundation Fellowship for Sculpture; 1952, Print Club of Philadelphia, 26th Annual Exhibition of Prints, Purchase Prize; 1953, Brooklyn Museum 7th Annual of Prints, Purchase Prize; 1953, Guggenheim Fellowship in Creative Printmaking; 1953, Wylon, International Society of Wood Engravers, Zurich, Switzerland; 1954, O'Hara Museum Prize, Japanese National Museum of Tokyo; 1961, Alonzo C. Mather Prize, Chicago Art Institute; 1961, São Paulo Bienal, Best Foreign Engraver; 1965, American Institute of Graphic Art, Special Medal of Merit; 1965, Pennsylvania Academy of the Fine Arts, Widener Medal; 1969 Gold Medal, National Institute of Arts and Letters

PUBLIC COLLECTIONS

Academy of Natural Science, Philadelphia, Pennsylvania; Albion College, Albion, Ohio; Alverthorpe Gallery, Jenkintown, Pennsylvania; Albright-Knox Art Gallery, Buffalo, New York; Allegheny College, Meadville, Pennsylvania; Art Institute of Chicago, Chicago, Illinois; Bezalel National Museum, Jerusalem; Brandeis University, Waltham, Massachusetts; Brooklyn Museum, Brooklyn, New York; Chase Manhattan Bank, New York; City Art Museum of St. Louis, St. Louis, Missouri; Wesleyan University, Middletown, Connecticut; Detroit Institute of Arts, Detroit, Michigan; Fitchburg Museum, Fitchburg, Massachusetts; Harvard University, Cambridge, Massachusetts; Holyoke Public Library, Holyoke, Massachusetts; University of Illinois, Champaign-Urbana, Illinois; Kunst Pä Arbeidsplassen, Oslo, Norway; Library of Congress, Washington, D.C.; Marshall College, Huntington, West Virginia; Mt. Holyoke College, South Hadley, Massachusetts; Munson-Williams-Proctor Institute, Utica, New York; Museum of Modern Art, New York; Museum of Fine Arts, Boston, Massachusetts; National Gallery of Art, Washington,

D.C.; Newark Museum, Newark, New Jersey; New School of Social Research, New York; New York Public Library, New York; Pennsylvania Academy of the Fine Arts, Philadelphia, Pennsylvania; Print Club of Philadelphia; Philadelphia, Pennsylvania; Princeton University, Princeton, New Jersey; Seattle Art Museum, Seattle, Washington; Smith College, Northampton, Massachusetts; University of Delaware, Wilmington, Delaware; University of Nebraska, Lincoln, Nebraska; Whitney Museum of American Art, New York; Worcester Art Museum, Worcester, Massachusetts; Yale University, New Haven, Connecticut

ONE-MAN EXHIBITIONS

1939, Glickman Studio Gallery, New York; 1940, Gallery of the New York University School of Architecture and Allied Arts, New York; 1951, Gallery "Numero," Florence, Italy; 1952, The Little Gallery, Princeton, New Jersey; 1952, Mount Holyoke College, South Hadley, Massachusetts; 1953, Fitchburg Art Museum, Fitchburg, Massachusetts; 1953, 1955, 1956, 1957, 1958, 1960, 1962, 1964, 1966, Grace Borgenicht Gallery, New York; 1952, 1953, 1957, 1959, 1960, 1962, 1964, 1965, 1967, Boris Mirski Gallery, Boston, Massachusetts; 1957, Worcester Art Museum, Worcester, Massachusetts; 1959, University of California, Berkeley, California; 1959, Philadelphia Print Club, Philadelphia, Pennsylvania; 1959, Pasadena Art Museum, Pasadena, California; 1961, Boymans Museum, Rotterdam, Netherlands; 1961, Amerika Haus, Berlin, Germany; 1961, Le Centre Culturel Americain, Paris, France; 1962, The Royal Watercolor Society with St. George's Gallery, London, England; 1962, Bowdoin College Museum of Art, Brunswick, Maine; 1966, Peale House, Pennsylvania Academy of the Fine Arts, Philadelphia, Pennsylvania

TEACHING POSITIONS

1953, Instructor in printmaking, Worcester Art Museum, Worcester, Massachusetts; 1953 to present, Professor in drawing, printmaking, and sculpture, Smith College, Northampton, Massachusetts

PRINTED AT THE MERIDEN GRAVURE COMPANY
TYPE SET BY THE STINEHOUR PRESS
DESIGNED BY LEONARD BASKIN

For my mom, Louisa
– Christine

For my boys, Markos and Filippos
– Niki

MIX
Paper from
responsible sources
FSC® C118365
FSC
www.fsc.org

Copyright © 2022 Clavis Publishing Inc., New York

Visit us on the Web at www.clavis-publishing.com.

No part of this publication may be reproduced or stored in a retrieval system,
or transmitted in any form or by any means, electronic, mechanical, photocopying,
recording, or otherwise, without the prior written permission of the publisher,
except in the case of brief quotations embodied in critical articles and reviews.
For information regarding permissions, write to Clavis Publishing, info-US@clavisbooks.com.

The Purple Pail written by Christine Ieronimo and illustrated by Niki Leonidou

ISBN 978-1-60537-658-5

This book was printed in October 2021 at Nikara, M. R. Štefánika 858/25, 963 01 Krupina, Slovakia.

First Edition
10 9 8 7 6 5 4 3 2 1

Clavis Publishing supports the First Amendment and celebrates the right to read.

Christine Ieronimo & Niki Leonidou

The Purple Pail

Clavis

NEW YORK

Ava brings her favorite pail
to the beach.

"A pretty shell!"

She rushes to put
it in Purple Pail.

A big wave sweeps it into the sea.

"Come back!"

Aoife spies Purple Pail, *buicéad corcra*, caught on the rocks.

"Mama, look!"

Aoife uses it to carry her tools.

A blustery wind blows Purple Pail,
tumbling it over the moors and into the ocean.

"Oh no!"

Afonso finds Purple Pail, *balde roxo*, bobbing in an inlet.

"I can use this when I dig for clams."

Afonso takes his clams to market.
He sells them to a fish peddler.

He sets Purple Pail near a boat.

"Wait!"

Amal spies Purple Pail,
satl 'urjwanium, near a wall.

"This will hold
my ginger!"

Amal carries her ginger roots to the market to sell. While she's busy, she leaves Purple Pail near a truck.

"Stop!"

Alemitu discovers Purple Pail,
hamirawi baldi, under a coffee tree.

**"I can fill this to the very top
with the red berries!"**

At home, Alemitu's mom roasts and grinds the beans. She pours the coffee for her family to celebrate the day.

Alemitu leaves Purple Pail at the coffee farm.

"Where did it go?"

Ashok stumbles upon Purple Pail, *bainganee baaltee.*
He crams it full of wildflowers.

"Now I can make
so many flower candles!"

Ashok displays his flower candles at the sacred river.
He accidentally bumps into Purple Pail,
knocking it into the water. Off it floats.

"No! Don't go away!"

On her walk, Asmida catches sight of
Purple Pail, *baldi ungu*, half buried in the sand.

"This is just what I need!"

Asmida dips the cloth into the colorful dyes.
Purple Pail disappears into a box of scarves.

"It was just here!"

Aroha stumbles across Purple Pail,
pere pāpura, on her way to her mailbox.

"This can hold my honeycomb."

While Aroha is checking her bees,
a wind blows Purple Pail into the river.

"Wait!"

Agustin rescues Purple Pail, *cubo morado*,
near a dock at the water's edge.

"I must show Papa!
We can use this for our grapes."

Purple Pail gets packed
into a delivery crate.

"I can't find it."

Antonio rescues Purple Pail, *cubeta morada*,
from the waves on the beach.

"I need this for my chocolates."

Purple Pail is packed in
a carton of chocolate bars.

"I just had it."

TULUM
CHOCOLATE
87% CACAO

"Mommy, can I have a pail, please,
Mommy, please?" Alex begs.

Alex's mom notices Purple Pail behind all
the other pails. She reaches for it.

"Alex, I think I know this pail."
As his mom holds the pail close, she and Alex
are transported around the world.

"Alex, this is my favorite Purple Pail.
I lost it years ago and now
it's yours to treasure."

Purple Pail

Ireland
Buicéad corcra
Boo-ked **kor**-krah

Portugal
Balde roxo
Bahl-dih **ruh**-show

Morocco
Satl 'urjwanium
Suh-**tool** ehr-**jwan**-ee-um

Ethiopia
Hamirawi baldi
Hah-mi-**rah**-wee **bahl**-dee

India
Bainganee baaltee
Beh-**gah**-nee **bahl**-tee

Malaysia
Baldi ungu
Bahl-dee **oon**-goo

New Zealand
Pere pāpura
Pay-ray pah-**poo**-rah

Chile
Cubo morado
Koo-bow maw-**rah**-dow

Mexico
Cubeta morada
Koo-**bay**-tah maw-**rah**-dah